Usborne

Get ready for school

First Colours
Sticker Book

You'll find all the stickers in the middle of the book.

This book belongs to:

- -

Illustrated by Marina Aizen

Designed by Claire Ever & Meg Dobbie. Words by Hannah Wood.

Lots of colours

Here are all the animals you'll meet in this book.
They are showing you their favourite colours.
Add all the colour stickers to the paintbox.

Eddie elephant

Leo lion

Can you find the **red** sticker?

Georgie giraffe

Red

Blue

Yellow

Green

Alfie alligator

Cassie cat

Toby tiger

Orange is my favourite! Can you find the orange sticker?

Rosie rabbit

Pink	Orange	White
Purple	Brown	Black

Zac zebra

Betsy bear

Hattie horse

4

Red

Leo lion is outside his house. Stick lots more red things on the picture.

Can you stick Leo's helmet on?

Blue

Eddie elephant is having tea by the sea. Add all the blue stickers.

Can you stick on
a blue bird?

MENU

Yellow

Georgie giraffe is having a picnic. Add a yellow
sun and some yellow food to the picture.

Green

Alfie alligator is working in his garden. Help him by putting all the stickers on the picture.

Purple

Hattie horse is going to bed. Use the purple stickers to finish the picture.

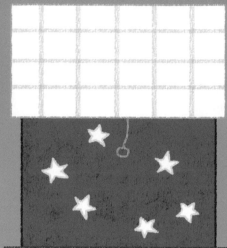

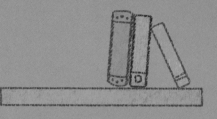

Can you stick on some purple toys?

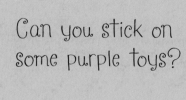

Pink

It's Cassie cat's birthday party. Stick some pink party food and presents on the picture.

Orange

Toby tiger is at the beach. Stick lots more orange things on the picture.

Brown

Betsy bear is at the market. Use the stickers to add more brown bread and pies to her stall.

Black

Zac zebra is cycling home. Add some black stickers to finish the picture.

Red (page 4)

Blue (page 5)

Yellow (page 6)

Green (page 7)

Purple (page 8)

Pink (page 9)

Orange (page 10)

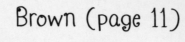

Brown (page 11)

Black (page 12)

White (page 13)

Hot-air balloons (pages 14-15)

Colour mixing (pages 20-21)

Counting colours (pages 22-23)

1	2
3	4
5	6
7	8
9	10

White

Rosie rabbit and her friends are playing in the snow.
Add the white stickers to finish this snowy scene.

Whoosh!

Hot-air balloons

Look at the colour of each basket, and add the balloon sticker that matches.

pink

white

red

yellow

blue

Add some more colourful stickers to the picture.

green

purple

orange

brown

black

Rainbow colouring

The animals are painting a rainbow. Fill in
each stripe with the colour that is written
on the paint can, then colour in
the rest of the picture.

red

orange

yellow

green

blue   purple

Fancy dress

The animals are dressing up. Look at the colours they are wearing and use the matching stickers to finish their outfits. Trace over the letters to write the name of each colour.

brown

orange

Can you guess what I'm going to be?

black

I'm wearing white fairy wings.

white

pink

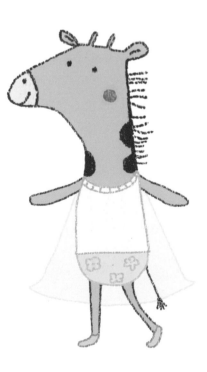

yellow

Colour mixing

Some colours can be made by mixing two or more other colours together.

What do these two colours make?

Purple

Orange

Green

Look at the two colours that each animal is going to mix together.
What colour will each painting be?

Add the stickers to show what the animals are going to paint.

Look at the colours on the paint pots, then use the splodge stickers to show what new colour will be made when you mix them together.

Pink

Grey

Brown

Can you guess what I'm painting?

This picture is going to be my favourite colour!

Counting colours

First use the stickers to finish this picture.

Next, how many of these things can you count?

Red chimneys	Blue glow bugs	Yellow windows	Green leaves	Orange bricks

Stick the answers in the boxes.

Purple flowers	Pink t-shirts	White stars	Brown birds	Black puffs of smoke

Fireworks display

Use the stickers to fill the sky with brightly-coloured fireworks.
Say what colour each one is.